Mr Mildew and the Duke

by Jeanne Willis

Illustrated by Zoe Sadler

OXFORD
UNIVERSITY PRESS

People liked Mr Mildew. It was hard not to.

He lived in an ancient house that belonged to the duke, which was filled with lots of pets.

However, they were not ordinary pets.

Mr Mildew's house is ancient. Ancient means very old. What might Mr Mildew's ancient house look like?

Mr Mildew had tadpoles in his teapot and newts in his sink.

Mr Mildew's pets were not ordinary. What kinds of animals do you think make ordinary pets?

He had a chimp
named Joe ...

a mule named Paul ...

and an elephant
named Eve.

Mr Mildew had rescued all of his pets. Eve ate the most. Mr Mildew gave her bales of hay and sacks of wheat to eat.

Mr Mildew was so popular, hundreds of people came from the town to visit him and his pets each month.

However, Mr Mildew was not popular with the duke who lived in a large house on the hill.

The duke did not like hundreds of people on his land.

"I blame Mr Mildew!" he said. "Why can't he keep normal pets?"

Mr Mildew was popular. Do you think the duke was popular? Why/Why not?

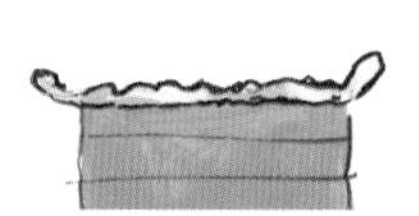
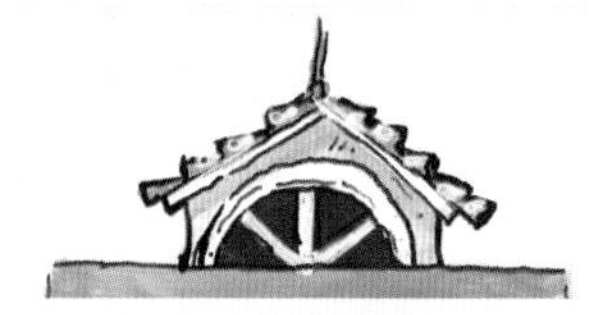

“What if his chimp escapes?” said the duke. “What if his mule kicks me? What if his elephant eats my crops?”

It is time to make
a few rules.

child
The duke went to Mr Mildew's home.
"Let me in!" he yelled.

"Good to see you!" Mr Mildew said to the duke. "Come in. I will make some tea."

The duke went in. He peered at the teapot. "You can't make tea," he said. "There are tadpoles in the teapot!"

"They needed a home," explained Mr Mildew.

"There are newts in the sink!" screamed the duke.

"Do sit down," said Mr Mildew.

"There's an elephant in my way!" cried the duke.

"You are in *her* way!" said Mr Mildew. "Feed her some hay and she will let you sit down."

Just then, Joe the chimp sprang off the shelf.
He jumped on to the duke.

"Joe is just playing," said Mr Mildew.
"Get off, Joe!" shouted the duke.

Paul, the mule, wandered in.

"You can ride him if you like," said Mr Mildew.

"I don't want to!" snapped the duke. "In fact, I have decided to create a new set of rules."

What kind of rules do you think the duke is going to create?

"I do not like all these pets and people on my land!" said the duke.
The duke started to read out his rules.

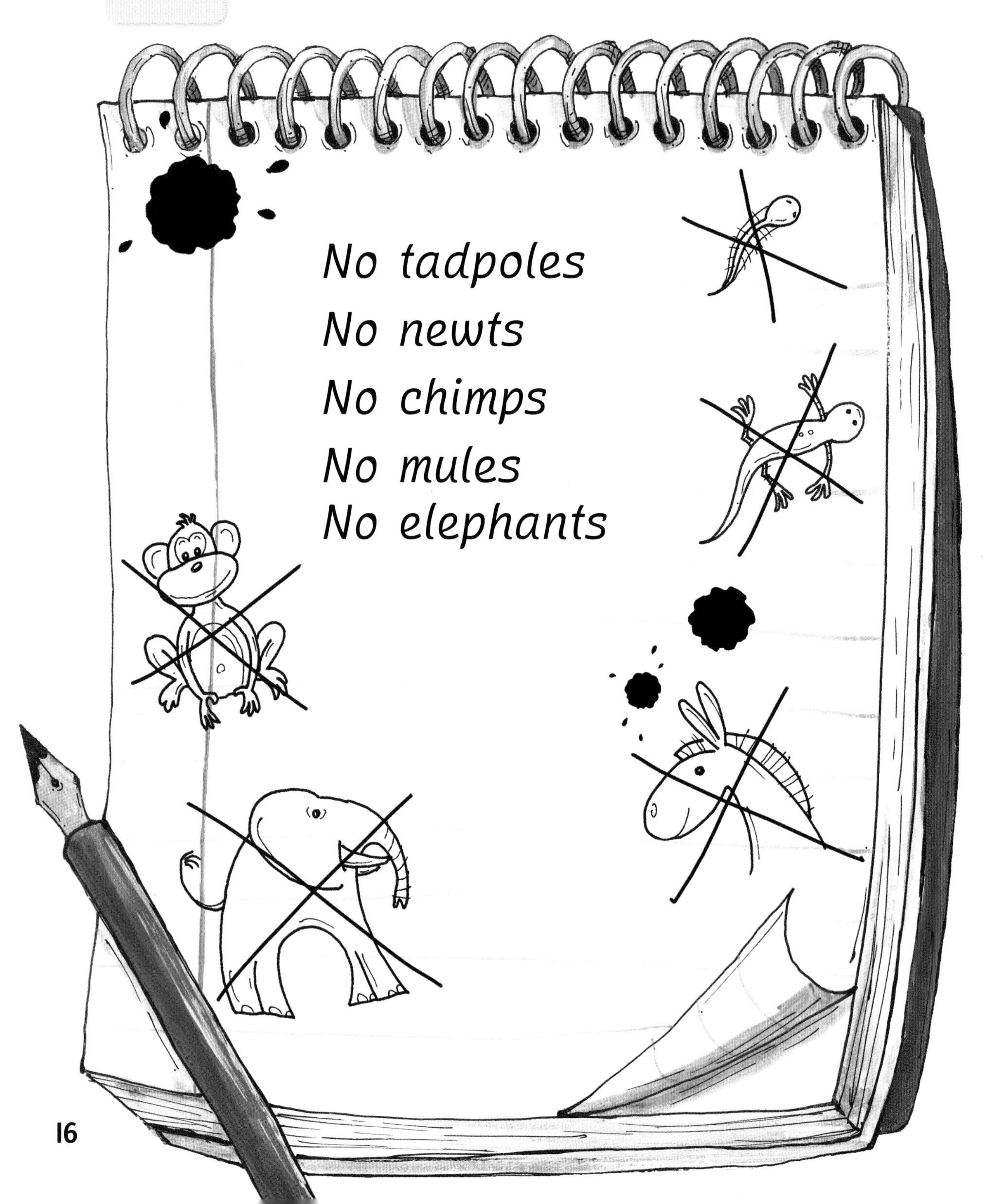
No tadpoles
No newts
No chimps
No mules
No elephants

"I do not like these rules," said Mr Mildew.
"What am I to do with all my pets?"

"You will have to get rid of your pets," said the duke.

"I can't," said Mr Mildew, looking sad.

"It's the rules," replied the duke. "Otherwise, get off my land!"

"In that case, goodbye!" said Mr Mildew.

He packed up and rode off into the sunset with his pets.

The duke says that Mr Mildew must follow the rules, otherwise he must leave. Does this mean Mr Mildew has to leave, or does he have another choice?

The next day ...

“Is Mr Mildew at home?” asked the people.

“No,” said the duke. “He left.”

"Tell him to come home," they cried.
"Impossible!" snapped the duke.
"Then we will go too," they said.

The duke says it would be impossible to ask Mr Mildew to come home. Does this mean it might happen or it cannot happen? Do you think it's really impossible?

All the people left.
The duke jumped with joy.
“Hooray,” he cried.

At first, the duke was glad to see the back of them all.

After a while, however, he became lonely.

"I will find Mr Mildew and ask him to come back," he said to himself.

The duke searched far and wide until he found Mr Mildew.

Mr Mildew had an amazing new home with all of his pets. He also had some new friends.

"Come back," said the duke. "I miss you!"

"This is our home now," said Mr Mildew, "but you can stay with us!"
"Are there rules?" asked the duke.
"No," said Mr Mildew. He handed the duke a key.
"Hooray!" cried the duke.

Match them up!

Read the names. Then match the characters to their names.

Mr Mildew

Paul

Joe

Eve

the duke

newts

tadpoles